Gran had come to stop.
"But I will not stop lon

Gran was good fun.
The children were glad she had come.

But Gran had hurt her arm.
She had to strap it up.

"Did you crack a block?" said Chip.

"Did you drag a truck?" said Biff.

"Did you snap a branch?" said Kipper.

"Did you trip on the step?" said Mum.

Gran had a big box.
"This is for you all," she said.

"You will like it," she said.
"Come and see."

It was a drum kit.

"Gran!" said Dad with a groan.

Dad was strict with Gran.
"No fuss and no tricks! You need to rest that arm," he said.

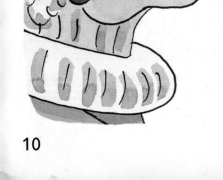

"Children!" said Gran.
"Quick, come and see this."

"What is it, Gran?" said the children.
"A spook," said Gran. "Look!"

The spook was under the tree.

It's an odd spook!

It was not a spook.
It was Gran's night dress with
a bright light under it.

"Gran!" said Dad. "I said no tricks."